Don't worry, be hoppy.

Wow! Yellow looks good on you!

pretty in pink

The dog ate my homework.

More cheese, please?

More cheese, please?

Who you calling "nutty"?

hogs & kisses

PSST, PASS IT ON...

Practically Purr-fect

Just Chilling

I'm ready for my close-up.

DOUBLE TROUBLE!

It's a good hare day!

Dogs beg. I *demand*.

You put your right paw in...

Are you fur real?